All the Ways I Speak

By Deena Muhammedali
Illustrated by TullipStudio

01

Dedicated to
all of my butterflies.

My name is Elora.
I am like a butterfly, shy and quiet on the outside.
But that doesn't stop me from flying.

I don't speak the way other kids do, so people don't always know how to talk to me. They think I have nothing to say.
But I actually have LOTS of words and ideas, and I can speak in many ways.

"More"

Sometimes I use
my hands to point or
use sign language.
Some signs that
I love to use are "more,"
"help," "all done," and
"thank you."

"All done"

"Help"

Will you try some of them with me?

"Thank You"

09

I also use something called a communication device. This has pictures and words that help me share what I'm thinking.

When I press a button, you can hear my words! Want to push the buttons with me?

I take this communication device with me everywhere I go.

It even has pictures of my family, my address, and my favorite things to order at restaurants.

At school, my communication device helps my friends and teachers see more of who I am.

It helps my personality shine through!

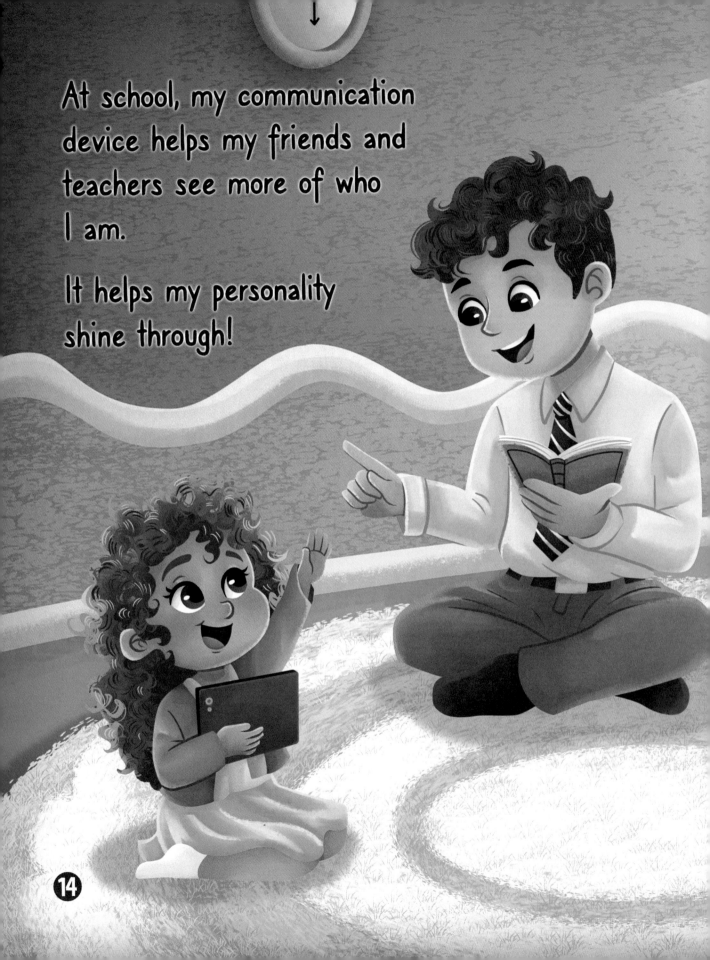

It is also how
I can answer questions,
let my teacher know when
I'm thirsty, and even ask to
use the restroom!

My face and
my body also
help me show how
I'm feeling.
I can smile, cry, and
laugh just like you.

16

I can nod and shake my head no. I can wave hello and goodbye.

Sometimes you will hear my real voice. I can't say full words the way that you do, but I can use the tone of my voice to show if I'm happy, sad, angry, or upset.
How do you feel today?

Happy

Sad

Shy

Angry

Tired

Hungry

Sleepy

Shocked

Sick

I also use something called a switch.
When I press it, my friends hear my favorite jokes.
Do you want to try?
I like to be funny, just like you.

Pictures help me communicate too!
My parents like to keep pictures around the house,
and I even have my own picture book to help me
share my wants and needs.

People aren't always sure if I'm smart. But I understand a lot, and I love when people talk to me. I will speak to you in one of my special ways.

I am grateful for my family, friends, therapists, and teachers.

They are always there for me.

I know that I'm different, but I love me for me.

And I hope you can love me for me, too.

27

My name is Elora.
I am like a butterfly, shy and
quiet on the outside.
But that doesn't stop me
from flying.

Although I may not use my words the same way you do, there are many ways that I can speak.

The End

About the Author

Deena Muhammedali is more than a Pediatric Speech-Language Pathologist; she's a dedicated advocate for all children, driven by a passion to make a positive impact on their lives.

All the Ways I Speak is inspired by the children she has worked with. She hopes that her story will raise awareness, promote acceptance, and help people embrace differences – to see others for their strengths and abilities rather than what is merely seen at first glance.

After all, we are more alike than different!
Deena believes that every voice, regardless of how it's expressed, deserves to be welcomed and heard.
In her free time, Deena likes to explore cafes, travel, enjoy nature, and spend time with her family.

72223515R00021